SECURITY IS A THUMB AND A BLANKET

BY CHARLES M. SCHULZ

SECURITY IS A THUMB AND A BLANKET
© 1963, 1971, 1982, 1983, 1984 by United Feature Syndicate, Inc.
All Rights Reserved
First paperback edition 1971
Revised, expanded paperback edition 1983
Based on "Security is a Thumb and a Blanket"
by Charles M. Schulz

Published by Determined Productions, Inc.
Box 2150, San Francisco, California 94126
Printed in Hong Kong

Distributed in U.K. by Attica Publications
A Division of Argus Communications, Harlow, Essex, England
ISBN 1-85176-002-4

The first edition of **SECURITY IS A THUMB AND A BLANKET,** written and illustrated by world-famous cartoonist Charles M. Schulz, appeared in 1963. Its immediate success followed the lead of the first best seller, HAPPINESS IS A WARM PUPPY.

Now the beloved PEANUTS® characters are back in a new, enlarged version of **SECURITY IS A THUMB AND A BLANKET.** You'll find the familiar blend of Schulz nostalgia and humour, but three times as many pages of cartoons and sentiments, all in colour. Snoopy and the entire PEANUTS® gang will warm your heart — again!

You'll also want to ask for the new and enlarged versions of HAPPINESS IS A WARM PUPPY, LOVE IS WALKING HAND-IN-HAND, I NEED ALL THE FRIENDS I CAN GET, CHRISTMAS IS TOGETHER-TIME **and** HOME IS ON TOP OF A DOG HOUSE.

Security is an album of happy memories.

Security is
knowing someone
will help you
with your
homework.

Security is a good watchdog.

Security is
never having
to eat lunch
by yourself.

Security is
learning to do
the things that are
expected of you.

Security is
finding
a new friend
at camp.

Security is
a friend who isn't
embarrassed
when you cry.

Security is a dressmaker who understands you.

Security is growing your own vegetables.

Security is an experienced pilot.

Security is
keeping
the ol' body
in shape.

Security is
riding
on the back
of your
mum's
bike.

Security is following a leader.

Security is being on a team with professionals.

Security is
getting a lot
of valentines.

Security is
being first in line
at the movies.

Security is a naturally dazzling smile.

Security is knowing all the steps.

Security is
a pair
of warm,
woolly socks.

Security is being a member of the club.

Security is
knowing someone
who wants
to put you on a
pedestal.

Security is
having "wheels."

Security is having friends you can trust.

Security is a well-stocked cupboard.

Security is
learning
not to be afraid.

Security is never missing a cue.

Security is a good secretary.

Security is
something
that helps you
stay afloat.

Security is
a new recipe book
for the cook.

Security is understanding an "in" joke.

Security is
being one
of the gang.

Security is
a good tan.

Security is
being the doctor
instead of the patient.

Security is knowing people who like houseguests.

Security is
three sharp pencils
and lots
of erasers.

Security is
an umbrella.

Security is believing in statehood, countryhood, cityhood and neighbourhood.

Security is a friend with a swimming pool.

Security is not having to eat out alone.

Security is
believing
in the
Great Pumpkin.

Security is knowing where you can get a pizza after midnight.

Security is having friends in high places.

Security is
a good
alarm system.

Security is
one thing
to one person
and another thing
to another person.

Security is
a full book
of phone
numbers.

Security is
having a friend
who likes to talk
on the phone
as long as
you do.

Security is
a strong
backhand.

Security is
having a friend
who knows
the answers.

Security is
knowing there'll
be someone
to catch you
if you fall.

Security is
a thumb
and a
blanket.

Security is
taking advantage
of every
opportunity.

Security is practicing sand shots.

Security is fastening your seat belt.

Security is
not having to worry
about where
you'll get dinner.

Security is
having someone
to lean on.

Security is
scoffing
fresh cookies
in front of a
warm TV.

Security is being smothered with kisses.

Security is
having a friend
who'll screen your
phone calls.

Security is
a night light.

Security is
having a list
when you go
Christmas
shopping.

Security is flight insurance.

Security is not having to worry about tomorrow.